Hopeful

Publishing Company, Inc.

FINDING THE WISDOM YOU SEEK

Hidden where you will never look

Michael R Holley

Published by Hopeful Publishing Company, Inc. Lakeland, FL. For volume discounts, institutional sales, corporate events or promotional use, send an inquiry email to **michael@michaelholley.com** or go to **www.hopefulpublishing.com**

Hopeful Publishing Company, Inc.
P.O. Box 7517
Lakeland, FL 33807
863-559-4049

NOTE TO READERS
In some instances, people or companies portrayed in this book are illustrative examples based on the author's experiences; not intended to represent a particular person or organization. While the publisher and author have used their best efforts in preparing this book for publication, they make no representations with respect to the accuracy or contents of this book.

Cover art painted by Laura Cooper Copyright © 2016 Hopeful Publishing Company

Library of Congress Cataloging-in-Publication Data

Holley, Michael R. 1960-

Finding The Wisdom You Seek is a fictional fable, self-help, spiritual, living guide to overcoming obstacles and adversity. Its intention is to help you see life from a different perspective, using the talents and wisdom you were born with.

Printed in the United States of America

ISBN: 098622863X
ISBN-13: 9780986228636
Library of Congress Control Number: 2016907861
Hopeful Publishing Company, Inc, Lakeland, FL

DEDICATION

To my wife, Hope, I love you! Thank you for your love, support and making my life complete.

To all who have floundered or stumbled, were able to get up, learn and become all they were intended to be - more importantly to all who will - this book is for you.

TABLE OF CONTENTS

INTRODUCTION

Meet Bob, a 47-year-old man, married to Barbra for almost 20 years, vice president of a manufacturing company. He has three children, all girls. He and Barbra were high school sweethearts who went their own separate ways during college, only to reconnect in their late 20s.

They live in an upscale gated community. Barbra has not worked since the girls were born, Bob has earned in excess of a six-figure income since making vice president. Bob was considered the up-and-comer in the company for years. And up until a few years ago, he was considered to be a top contender for the CEO/President slot when the current CEO retires.

Over the last few years, for reasons not known or understood, it is widely considered by the employees (and probably the executive level as well) that Bob is coasting, hoping to make it to retirement. That is surprising, given his age and the fact he is the only executive with young children and seems to spend a lot of what he makes on his family's high lifestyle.

Barbra is still a beautiful woman who was at the top of their community's social scene, as well as highly visible at everything involving the children. She too seems to have withdrawn somewhat from the social scene, while doing much for and with the children.

This is a traditional family, with traditional values who should be on top of the world, yet everyone notices - but them - they seem to be going through the motions and are much less happy than in times past. Even the children, who worship their dad, have made comments that they just do not do as much as a family as they used to. The family picnics and outings that were so common with their dad's company seem to have become less frequent and now are nonexistent.

Just a few weeks ago, the oldest daughter was shocked to learn that these family functions sponsored by their dad's company had actually been generated and organized by Bob's office. A friend whose dad also worked at the company wondered aloud why something so popular had stopped.

In this book we will look at what happened to Bob's work and family life when he stopped growing personally, if not retreating, and sought solutions rooted in bad thought and unhealthy judgment.

Here is Bob's journey to find what was never lost …

"Knowing yourself is the beginning of all wisdom."

— Aristotle

1

THE DARKNESS BEFORE THE LIGHT

It had been a long week in the office, it was Friday, Bob was to go home and have dinner with his family. Nevertheless, he was a bundle of nerves and this was not what he desired to do, at least not at this moment. Therefore, he decided going home at this instant would be a disservice to his family. Certainly my children do not want to see me like this was how he justified his decision. He was using his increasing bad judgment to justify bad decisions.

He called his friend Tom, the call went straight to voicemail. He then recalled Tom was out of the country trying to *find himself* or something. Bob thought a quick stop by the corner bar would be good for all concerned. He ordered his usual, a double Scotch on the rocks.

In what seemed like only a few minutes, his phone started ringing. He let it go to voice mail. Then it rang again. He again let it go to voice mail. Then the text came, *"You promised the children you would cook out for them, then pop popcorn and watch a movie tonight before their bed time. It is now 8:30 and you are nowhere to be found, your assistant said you left for home at 6."*

Bob paid the bill, it was almost $50, how many had he had? He could not remember; he just knew he had to get home. He started his Mercedes, backed out of the parking space and decided to miss the traffic on the busy street and take the alley. It was empty of traffic and no one was turning into the alley from the street. Great, this would save five minutes.

Turning hard right and accelerating, Bob heard a scream, slamming on the breaks, the car almost magically stopping in an instant. Right in front of his car in the middle of his windshield was a woman pushing a baby carriage. She was screaming at the top of her lungs.

How did he not see her? He slammed the car into park and jumped out in almost the same motion. The front bumper of the Mercedes was pressed against the baby carriage, the baby was crying louder than any baby he had ever heard and he had three children. Just another inch and the baby carriage would have been under the front bumper, taking the baby with it.

The baby was unharmed but startled, either from the car touching the carriage or the mother's panicked and continuing screams. The mother screamed as loud as she could, "Are you drunk or just blind?" Beginning to cry the mother said, "You almost killed us!"

She picked the baby up out of the carriage and held her as she had never held her before. A business owner peeked out the back of his business and asked if everything was all right. Bob said nothing, just stood by the fender of the car looking at the mother and baby, trying to grasp what had almost happened. She said between sobs, "We are fine, I think, no thanks to this idiot." All Bob could utter was, "I am so sorry. I am so thankful you are both OK." The woman then started slowly walking into the night, holding the baby tightly and pushing the carriage.

Bob, returning to the Mercedes, very slowly idled down the alley that was to have saved him so much time. Thinking about what had just happened, replaying the scene in his mind over and over. He then started crying and just wanted to be home with his wife and children, constantly looking in his rear-view mirror for the police officer he was sure the lady or business owner had called.

He then pulled into the driveway of his huge house, so glad to be home, and opened the garage door to hurriedly park his Mercedes, only to see his wife's SUV not parked in its normal spot. Where could they have gone? She must have driven to the store, he thought. Where else could she have gone this late knowing he would be home any minute? He closed the garage and went inside, dialing his wife's cell phone as he walked.

It was now after 9 p.m., still time to watch a move with the children. He opened the side door to the huge kitchen, speechless as to what he saw: balloons and posters in his children's writing. The first one he saw said, "Happy end-of-week party daddy!" Another said, "Happy Weekend, glad you're home." Bob just started crying as he listened to his wife's cell phone go to voice mail.

Then on the refrigerator, he saw a full sheet of paper, in his wife's beautiful handwriting. "I could not bear to sit here and listen to the children cry about you missing their end-of-week surprise party for you. The meal they made you is in the microwave, we are going to my mom's for the weekend, please do not call."

Bob again dialed his wife's cell, then repeatedly, all with the same results: voice mail. He grabbed his key fob off the table and started to the garage, stumbling over the door edge and almost falling. He knew he had had too much to drink to drive to his mother-in-law's, some 40 miles and almost an hour away. He was already lucky not to be in jail, unsure, if not paranoid, someone might have gotten his tag number and the police could show up at any minute.

"Turn your wounds into wisdom."

— Oprah Winfrey

2

THE DARKEST MOMENT IS THE UNKNOWN

Bob awoke to the doorbell, followed by a hard knock, followed by a harder knock. In his foggy state, he first thought, and then said under his breath, "Oh my God it is the police." He did not even notice that it was daylight. He must have fallen asleep on the couch, crying himself to sleep last night, he determined. He felt awful, thought maybe it is the police and he should not open the door and if it is Barbra she would have used the garage entrance. Parting the living room curtains to peek out, Bob saw nothing on the street.

Looking out the peephole, he saw Tom standing there. In a haze, he opened the door and looked at Tom. Bob could not believe he was seeing the same friend he had seen a few weeks ago. Tom looked different.

With a somber look on his face, Tom finally cracked a smile and said, "Bob you look like hell; did you sleep in those clothes?"

Bob replied, "Yes, I fell asleep on the couch, Barbra took the kids and went to her mother's last night."

Tom replied, "Yes, I know, she sent me a text. I saw it last night as soon as I landed and was walking to baggage claim."

Bob said, "So you just got home?"

"Yes, last night about midnight. I called and came over, knocked on the door, you did not answer. I assumed you had gone to bed."

Bob said, "Let's make some coffee, I have something to tell you."

Bob then very somberly recounted the night's events. Tom just sat, shaking his head. "Bob," said Tom, "that is why I am here, Barbra said she cannot go on living like she is living and you will not go on living like you are. You are overweight. You drink too much. Your job is stressing you out more and more each week. It is obvious to everyone you no longer enjoy your work, and you never spend any quality time with your family. Bob, you are my friend but you are the oldest almost 50-year-old man I have ever seen. Barbra and the kids are worried about you and I know you are a train wreck looking for a place to happen. You could be and probably should be in jail right now!"

Bob just started sobbing, quietly first and then uncontrollably.

Tom said, "Bob get yourself together we are going for a drive. Go freshen up, put on some gym shorts, T-shirt, and tennis shoes. Let's go, right now."

Bob said nothing, he just got up, wiping tears from his puffy face, and did as he was told. A few minutes later, he popped out of the bedroom into the living room looking slightly better, not much, looking more as if he was ready for a jog.

Bob asked, "Where are we going?" as he sat somewhat frumpy in the front passenger seat of Tom's car.

"Do not concern yourself with that, it is not that far and it isn't like you have anything else to do." Bob started crying again.

Tom then asked, "Bob do you even know where I went?"

Bob answered, "Something or someplace about finding yourself is all I remember, was it an exotic island or something?"

Tom, half-laughing, said, "Not exactly. I went to India and then hiked the Himalayas. I was gone three weeks. Did you miss me?"

Bob said, "Wow, you went where? You have been gone for three weeks?"

Tom said, "Great friend you are, you did not remember where I went and did not even know or remember that I was gone for three weeks." Bob just looked at the floorboard, saying nothing.

Tom said to Bob, "There are two bottles of water at your feet, drink both of them. I have added some herbs and all-natural supplements to help clear your head."

Under his breath, Bob said, "He has been in the Himalayas for three weeks and now he is a pharmacist."

"What did you say?"

"Nothing, I am drinking it!"

After a 30 minute or so drive, they were on the outskirts of town. Tom pulled into a wooded area that looked like a park. It had a nice fence and a beautiful entrance but no gate and only a small sign that said, "Enter with permission only."

"Where are we?" Bob asked.

Tom responded, "We are at a place to clear your head so you can make some life-changing and hopefully life-saving decisions."

Tom parked the car in what looked to Bob like the middle of a forest out of a storybook: tall trees, beautiful flowers, birds singing, bees buzzing and small animals moving about the undergrowth.

Tom said, "Bob, let's go for a walk."

They started walking down a trail not saying anything. Bob, in his hungover state, was starting to get a clearer head. Was it the water, the herbs, this place? He was not sure but he felt better, the fresh air was helping.

They walked for 20 or 30 minutes and came to a clearing surrounded by big trees and a small brook running through the corner of the clearing. They could still hear the birds singing, much fainter now.

A large tree was lying on its side and Tom sat down on it, motioning for Bob to do the same. Bob sat down beside Tom and said, "Tom, what is all this about, why have you brought me here?"

Tom, looking relaxed and calm but serious, said in a very composed, cool but firm voice, in a very low tone, "Bob you almost killed someone - two someones - last night. Barbra has left you and she does not even know about last night's event.

"I want you to sit here and I am going to tell you about my last three weeks and what led up to that trip that changed my life forever."

"By three methods we may learn wisdom: first, by reflection, which is noblest; second, by imitation, which is easiest; and third by experience, which is the bitterest."

— Confucius

3

THE AWAKENING OF WHAT WE DO NOT KNOW

Tom began: "I too was having trouble at work as you have been. I too have been drinking too much, you know this because much of it was with you. I have been unable to keep a girlfriend. I felt awful all the time, my health, my mental state was deteriorating. A friend told me about this place and arranged for me to come here to clear my head. I was coming here on weekends for months. One Saturday, I met a stranger, a youthful-looking older man, on the same path we just walked. He and I sat right where we are sitting. He explained to me I needed a change in perspective, a new or different outlook on life, to get reacquainted with the real me that everyone used to love to be around. I needed to learn some universal principles of life that I had yet to discover."

Bob started to speak and Tom held up a finger and continued, "At the end of the long conversation that Saturday, after covering philosophy, health, relationships, inner wisdom, unhealthy thoughts, spirituality, universal principles of life, judgment unbecoming of my character and life's overall experiences, the man asked a question: 'If you could go anywhere in the world, a place you only dreamed of, to reboot your perspective and thinking, to *see* the unseen, to *hear* the unheard, to experience and feel life as never before, to find what you have not found, where would it be?'

"Then it just popped into my head: India, the Himalayas, yes, the Himalayas, that was it," Tom said, 'I have always heard and read that people travel there to find and feel, but especially to discover, the wisdom and true happiness that has been so elusive.'

"After I said that to the stranger, he nodded his head in agreement, reached into his trousers, and pulled out a business card. He asked me, 'How are you financially, can you do this, I mean, are you financially able to make a trip like this on short notice?'

"I told him, 'I am no millionaire, however, I think I have enough money in the bank to cover it. I have no idea what this costs, but I would guess that it would not be an issue.'

"My new, wise friend said, 'Great,' and handed me the card and said, 'Call this number and they will make the arrangements, I can assure you it is safe and you will come back a different man, how much of a different man depends greatly on you.''

"I thanked the man and shook his hand, then I looked away for just a second, to pull out my wallet and put the business card in it for safe keeping. When I turned around to tell the man, "Thank you,' he was gone. I never got his name and when I called out for him, there was no answer.''

"I thought about him all the rest of that day and every day since and came up with a nickname for him, 'The Engager.' He got me engaged in looking deeper into myself and the purpose of my life and I'll always be grateful for that. I only hope to meet with him again, so I might thank him for beginning my enlightenment."

"I called the number that very afternoon to leave a message, after all, it was Saturday. A woman answered and I thought she said something about 'Clearing the Mind Travels,' or something like that. I relayed that a man gave me the number. She asked if I had a valid passport and I said I did. She then asked me how my name appeared on my passport and did I have travel dates in mind? I said I would like to leave the following weekend, give myself a week to wrap up things at work and let my boss and coworkers know I was taking time off."

Bob just sat there listening as if he were listening to his favorite teacher or professor, giving his total undivided attention to his longtime friend.

Tom looked at Bob and said, "Bob, you are my friend, you are my best friend, I have changed my life forever and now it is the time that I help you change your life forever. I was on the phone with Barbra several times last night, I told her you would never agree. I knew this was a complete waste of time until you told me the story of what happened when leaving the bar. Bob, this is your destiny!"

Bob, looking a little white-faced and very perplexed, said, "What is my destiny?"

Tom then said, "You are going to make a similar trip, discover what is out there that you so desperately seek, to save your life and your marriage."

Bob jumped to his feet, looking shocked, "What about Barbra and the children, my job? I have responsibilities, I am an executive with people looking up to me, Tom, you are crazy!"

Tom pointed for Bob to sit back down. "Bob you almost killed a baby and her mom last night. In the blink of an eye, just one more inch, you could be facing life in prison right now. Your wife left you last night. Those people looking up to you see the same train wreck of an executive that those who love you see. Do you not see; can you not hear your inner self crying for help? If not now, when? If not there, then where? This is your destiny! There is a good man inside you, it is time to rediscover him!"

Tom calmed his voice back to the demeanor of a seasoned monk and said, "Bob, if you do this, Barbra and the children will be waiting at home with open arms on your return. If not, I am not sure what happens."

Bob sat down and actually calmed down very quickly, then said in a quiet, almost sheepish voice, "Tom, please tell me more about what made you look so different, what did you see, what did you learn, what made you look and act so different?"

"Bob, my experience was my experience, your experience will be your experience," Tom continued. "Why don't you tell me what you felt last night with that lady and baby in your windshield, to get home and see all the posters and made-up surprise party waiting for you that you missed. What did you feel while you were sitting on the couch crying, not knowing if your wife was coming home or not, waiting and wondering if the police would be knocking at your door? Tell me what you thought, what you dreamed and how you felt."

Bob, looking like a timeworn, overweight man with a puffy face and a big tear rolling down his face, said, "I saw someone I did not know. I saw someone I did not like. I saw my child as a baby in that stroller, thinking I would kill anyone who almost did that to my baby. I thought, 'Where did the man go who was once thought of as a great daddy, employee of the year, the up-and-coming company executive, the rumored future CEO?

"Now look at me, I'm just a fat, unhealthy, crappy dad who drinks too much and is not much fun to be around. What happened to the guy who you liked and respected, who my wife and children loved? Tom, what happened to me, I'm only 48 years old and I look and feel 70?"

Tom placed his hand on Bob's shoulder and looked him dead in the eye, and with his best Tibetan monk monotone voice, said, "The man we all love and care about is still in there and everyone knows it but him. Your wife, your children, your best friend, all your employees and co-workers, they are all rooting for you, it is the time my friend, time to *seek that which you have not found.*"

"The saddest aspect of life right now is that science gathers knowledge faster than society gathers wisdom."

— Isaac Asimov

4

THE JOURNEY TO FIND THE ANSWERS

The temperature was around freezing when Bob and his guide left the buses, taxis and bicycles behind.

Bob reviewed in his mind what he had read on the trip over: The Himalayan Mountain region of India is a geography of superlatives: high mountains, deep gorges, wild forest, and rolling high plateau. It is one of the most bio-diverse areas in the world. The climate is one of extremes, experiencing predominately winter and summer, from beautiful foliage in the summer to parts of the mountains that remain frozen in ice and snow year-round.

Then there are the people. The Himalayas are populated with more than 40 million people of diverse cultures and ancestry who have adapted to surviving in the environment. The main religions practiced in the region are Hinduism, Buddhism, and Islam. Hindus believe the Himalayas to be the abode of God.

Leaving the comfort of his hotel in Leh, India, the city of his arrival by airplane, Bob then took a bus, then taxi, to meet his guide. They were now on foot walking up a winding trail to who knows where. The guide spoke very good English with a heavy Indian accent. He was very quiet and hardly spoke, even when spoken to.

Bob asked, "How far do we plan to go today, what do we plan to see on the way?"

The guide, without missing a step, said, "I do not know. We will know what we see when we see it and we will stop where we stop when we arrive." Then he returned to his total silence.

After many hours, the sun was lower in the sky. Bob said, more or less to himself, "I would guess it is about 2 or 3 p.m., and I have to guess." No cell phone, no watch, nothing but a knapsack with a sleeping bag, water, bread and some local provisions packed by the guide's wife. The guide carried the same.

Bob thought, if I live through this, I am going to kill Tom. Then his mind wandered. What if I get separated from the guide? What if he were to drop dead of a heart attack? What if I have a heart attack? The one consolation was the sheer beauty of the surroundings. With the cool air, the crystal-clear sky, the trees, the leaves, the flowers, were all so bright and stunningly beautiful.

About the time Bob came around from his thoughts, becoming reacquainted with his surroundings, the guide stopped about ten feet ahead of him.

He asked, "What is it?"

No response.

He took the last steps to stand beside the guide.

It was the most beautiful sight he had ever seen. The sky was so blue; they were standing at a tree line that opened up to a clearing that could be hundreds of acres or more in size. Above them were snow covered mountains much more beautiful than any he had ever seen in America. The view looked more like a picture or a movie than any place he had ever been in his life, he suddenly had a great feeling about this place so far from home.

Bob asked the guide, "Is this where we stop for the night?"

No response.

Bob, thinking the guide was just caught in the moment, stood beside him quietly admiring his new surroundings.

Then, in the distance, a half-mile to a mile away, just visible beside the trail, was a big rock or boulder. Maybe 8 or 10-foot-high, could be a little more, it appeared to be the direction the guide was looking. Bob focused on the boulder, then almost yelled out, biting his tongue and remaining quiet. It appeared, even from this distance, to be a man sitting on a rock.

Bob started walking, drawn by some strange curiosity. He walked slowly and cautiously, without fear. The trail would wind a little around bushes or small rocks but was generally headed in the direction of the boulder with the man perched on the top like a gatekeeper.

Bob noticed over his shoulder the guide had started advancing also, but more slowly than Bob. About halfway between the tree line and the man, Bob stopped. Looking hard, Bob could see it was clearly a man atop the rock dressed in a light-colored robe. Just sitting with his legs crossed and his arms resting on his lap. It was hard to see what he was doing, if anything, other than sitting there, in some kind of meditative position.

After several minutes, the guide caught up to Bob and stopped beside him. Bob asked, "Do you know or recognize him?" The guide just shook his head no.

Bob then asked, "Does the robe look familiar or mean anything?"

The guide slowly started talking, "I do not recognize the man, not from this distance. I have not seen that robe, to the best I can see, that means nothing. There are hundreds or thousands of monks, hermits, priests, hermitages and monasteries throughout these mountains. That is why you are here, yes?"

"Yes," Bob said and started casually walking forward to the man on the rock, in no hurry to cover the remaining distance. The guide advanced even more slowly, thereby increasing the distance between them.

Bob arrived at the rock with the guide some distance behind him, however, close enough to hear what was said.

Bob, as humbly and as quietly as he could without whispering, asked, "Are you one of the monks who live up here?"

There was no response and no movement.

Bob looked back at the guide, who had not moved from his stopping point. Bob then half-joking and half curious, asked, "Are you OK, that rock looks very uncomfortable?"

Not even knowing if the man spoke English, he truly did not know what to do.

Bob thinking to himself. This man looks like the most spiritual man I have ever met and everyone I have met since arriving in this country has been so nice, I am just going to talk.

So Bob, in a quiet and friendly voice, started telling the man on the rock his story about working too much, neglecting his family, almost killing the mother and little baby, his wife leaving him, his best friends' trek to this area and his feeling there was more to life than he was living. After rambling, crying and emotionally bearing his soul and life, he stood still and decided to be quiet.

After what seemed like 30 minutes or so, with the sun getting low in the sky, Bob truly did not know what else to do. The guide was now sitting on the ground with his legs crossed drinking water. All of a sudden Bob realized how thirsty he was.

He looked at the man on the rock and said, "I am most humbly sorry for interrupting your time in this most beautiful place. My most humble apologies for bothering you, sir."

Just as Bob made a move to go back toward the guide, the old man spoke, not opening his eyes or moving a muscle. He spoke quietly, in English, with a strong, steady voice, in much the same tone Tom had spoken to Bob in the forest: "*You are what you seek.*" Then the old man again went silent.

Bob was surprisingly unafraid. He said, "Sir, I have traveled far to find what I do not know and how to straighten out my life, but with no disrespect, I am the last person that I seek."

As Bob started to walk away, the man again spoke in the same tone and volume as before, again without moving a muscle his eyes closed: "*You are what you seek, the secret lies within.*"

"The heart of a fool is in his mouth, but the mouth of a wise man is in his heart."

— Benjamin Franklin

5

"YOU ARE WHAT YOU SEEK"

Bob did not know what to say or what to do, he certainly was not going to get into an argument with an old man on a rock at sundown in who knows where.

The man then slowly and without moving a muscle opened his eyes. Again, very quietly and in the same tone, he asked, "Was your friend through here on his travels?"

Bob replied, "I really do not know, he did not tell me about his trip, he was here three weeks and told me I needed to make a similar trip, he said we would talk more when I returned."

The old man looked straight into his eyes with the clearest and brightest eyes Bob had ever seen in an old man. "Your friend said you could find the answers you seek here in these mountains?"

Bob thought long and hard before answering. "No, he really never said that, come to think of it. He just said I needed to make the journey and we would talk about his experience when I returned. He said, 'My experience was my experience and your experience will be yours.' In hindsight, it is hard to believe that I agreed to make such a journey on such little information. I feel a little foolish."

The old man spoke again, even more softly, "This friend sounds like a wise man who cares for you deeply."

Bob did not know what to say so he said nothing. The old man then, for the first time, moved his right arm, removing it slowly from his lap. He motioned toward the guide; as if by silent command, the guide started walking toward the rock.

The old man said to the guide, "You may leave him now, he will be with me, return to this rock in seven days." The guide, while saying nothing, returned to where he had been sitting, gathered the things he had unpacked and started down the trail.

Bob said nothing and was in an amazingly good state of mind, having no fear, only curiosity. He felt safe, he felt at peace having a feeling in his heart, way deep in his soul, that his life was about to change forever.

The old man then climbed down the rock with the agility of a mountain climber and the speed of a much younger man. He started walking up the path, rapidly, Bob followed, like a little puppy following his master to the food dish.

"Knowing others is intelligence;
knowing yourself is true wisdom.
Mastering others is strength;
mastering yourself is true power."

— Lao Tzu

6

SEEKING THE WISDOM OF THOSE WISER

J ust after dark, they arrived in a small compound made up of small buildings, Bob could not tell what they were made of. There were a few people mingling around, in total silence, wearing similar robes. It was cold now and he did not know how they were not freezing. He had put on his heaviest jacket and was still not warm.

The old man took Bob to what appeared to be the smallest of the structures, basically a hut. Inside was a cot, a pitcher of water, a hot cup of tea, a small bowl of some type of fruit and a loaf of bread. It was as if he or someone had been expected. The old man then was gone with no verbal instructions. Bob was so thirsty and tired he did not question. He took his hiking boots off, laid his jacket on the floor, drank the water, then the hot tea, ate the bread and then fell into the deepest sleep of his life.

As he was sleeping, he thought or dreamed he heard a baby crying, followed by a woman's scream. He sat straight up on the cot. It was as quiet a night as he had ever experienced. He must have been having a nightmare. He laid his head back down on the cot, again he was soon in a deep sleep.

He awoke very early, before daylight, and put on his shoes and jacket and walked out of the hut onto the compound. He heard some dishes clanking or something coming from a structure in the center of the buildings. It appeared to be the largest on the compound, even though it was not that large.

As he entered the building, maybe a dozen or so people sat around a big wooden table in a room eating. The old man, his presumed host, was sitting closest to the door he entered. He waved in a slow motion for Bob to sit next to him. He poured him something warm that appeared to be a tea with a unique smell.

Bob took a drink and it was warm and soothing, it tasted different than last night's tea, different than anything he had ever drank. It is not that it was good but very soothing. He was then handed a plate with bread similar to what he had the night before, with some kind of berries on the plate like none he had ever seen.

He ate and drank in silence as no one else was speaking. He finished about the time everyone started getting up, and he got up as well. Plates were gathered and, as quickly as everyone stood up, the table was clean and everyone started out the door. The old man, who Bob suspected was the gatekeeper to spiritual enlightenment, started walking to the edge of the compound and Bob followed.

Upon reaching the edge of the compound, the man placed his hand on Bob's shoulder and asked, "What brings you here to this place so far from home?"

Bob was thinking rapidly, does the old man not remember yesterday's conversation? Does he not remember the wreck of a life I left behind, coming here to find a solution to my troubles? So Bob thought for what seemed an eternity. The man did not seem impatient with Bob at all. Quite the contrary, he seemed willing to wait forever for the answer to his question.

Bob then said, as calmly and as softly as his voice could muster, "I seek the wisdom of those wiser, I seek the guidance of those more experienced, I seek the tranquility and calmness that my friend found in these parts of the world." Bob was surprised by his answer. He was not exactly sure where that had come from, but it seemed to sum up all that he hoped to experience.

The old man then surprised him, in his usually calm voice, repeating exactly what he had said the day before on the trail: *"You are what you seek, the secret lies within."*

Bob started to talk and then hesitated. Thinking more with his heart than his brain, Bob replied from deep inside his soul, "OK sir, I accept that I have traveled all this way to seek what is already inside me and that the secret to repairing my life lies within me. Is there some kind of special key or technique to open or access what is inside me?"

After a very long pause, the old man said, "Yes." Another long pause, then, "Gather your bag from the hut and follow me." With that, the old man started walking out of the compound.

Bob, excited as a school boy, hurriedly gathered his bag from the hut and caught up to the old man who was walking much more briskly than the day before.

Bob enthusiastically said, "Well, tell me and I will not have to bother you anymore."

The old man stopped abruptly and looked Bob straight in the eyes as he had done the previous day. The old man then said, with the patience and calmness of the Tibetan monks who inhabited these mountains, "Bob, *we* do not have the answers, only *you* have the answers." He then started walking again.

Bob was stunned, he did not remember telling the old man his name. I have the answers, what does that mean? What do I know? Am I right back where I started? Bob rushed to catch up with the man who was walking even more briskly than before.

Bob fell in behind him and kept pace, thinking at this point he should remain quiet and see where they were going. They walked for what seemed like a couple of hours, stopping at a brook to drink some of the coldest, freshest water Bob had ever drank in his life.

Then, just as suddenly as he stopped to rest and drink, the old man started walking again, going higher into the mountains. They were walking at a pace an experienced mountain hiker would have found challenging.

"Yesterday I was clever, so I wanted to change the world. Today I am wise, so I am changing myself."

— Rumi

7

WITHOUT A RUDDER, YOU HAVE NO DIRECTION

J ust when Bob thought he would collapse, the old man stopped. He said to Bob in a very quiet voice, "You are entering one of the most tranquil parts of all of these mountains. You are entering the serenity so many seek."

The trail opened up a bit. On the edge of the clearing was a small log cabin. It was bigger than most of the huts or buildings in the compound, but not by much.

The old man walked toward the cabin at a much slower and quieter pace. He stepped onto the front porch, looking around and listening like a wild animal around a pond before they drink. He almost glided to the door, opening the door in the same motion as walking. Bob thought this man is much more than he appears, mystical could not even come close to describing the aura around him. It was as if your grandfather was a mystic, Tibetan monk, Dalai Lama, and high priest, all in one body, that you are following through lands only God could have created.

As the old man entered the room, he walked to the fireplace, where there was neatly stacked firewood all cut with precision. Bob looked at the single room, a couple hundred square feet at the most. In one corner, by the fireplace, were a number of cots, and in another corner was more firewood and what looked like farming and building tools.

In just minutes the mystical old man had a fire going. Bob didn't notice how he started it. His new friend pulled out a large leather pouch from his robe. He asked quietly, "Are you hungry?"

Bob replied, "I think so, are we staying here tonight?"

The old man, looking most relaxed and at home, answered, "Yes. We will rest, eat, warm up and see what tomorrow's sunrise brings."

Bob was curious but had a warm spot in his heart for this place. It was the most surreal place he had been in his life, with probably the most spiritual and wisest man he had ever met. Bob was fine with whatever was to be.

They sat, eating from the leather pouch and enjoying the warmth of the now-building fire. Bob did not care or notice what he was eating. Bob then humbly asked a question, "Sir, is this where I am to find the answers I seek; the key, if you will, to what lies within?" There was a very long pause, not measurable in time. Bob was in no hurry for the answer. The old man seemed to meditate before speaking.

"Bob," he said, "you are a good man with a good heart, your soul is lost but knows it wishes to be found. You have come far, left a wonderful family and friend behind who care and worry that you find that which you seek. I feel your desire. I feel your past pain. I feel the need to find that which you are certain that you have lost. I cannot say for certain if you will find that which you seek since you brought it with you," he paused, letting what he said sink in. Then he added, "you have yet to discover your hidden gifts, the God-given talents, tools and wisdom you were born with."

Bob looked as if he had seen a ghost. How did this man he just met know so much about him? All he could muster was, "Please go on, I wish to hear, I wish to know more."

The old man continued, "As you go to sleep tonight in these humble but ample surroundings, sleeping in this surreal forest that most only dream of ever experiencing, think about what made you a great father, husband, businessman, student, child and sibling. What made you the kind of friend that another friend would be willing to share and wish you to experience his most unforgettable life experience? What was it others saw and followed? Most importantly, what was it you saw and liked most about yourself? When you awake we will discuss and I will share my thoughts on finding the key to the treasures and gifts you feel you have lost, or never had, and have traveled so far to find.

"Now you should sleep. We will talk when the sun rises and these tranquil surroundings come alive with all that is great in this part of the world."

Bob began to speak his thanks for this experience and this old man's kindness, but feeling that the old man already knew his thoughts, he just headed to one of the cots to rest.

Bob wanted to meditate on all he had experienced so far, instead, he fell asleep almost upon hitting the cot. In a deep sleep, Bob began to dream, not just any dream but a detailed dream, as real as if he were there.

Bob, his lovely wife, and three beautiful children were standing on a dock admiring a brand new boat, a yacht, most would call it. She must have been 80 feet long, shiny as the sun she was basking in. The children and Barbra were almost giddy with excitement, as a few crew members appeared to be running around preparing for their departure. "All aboard," Bob yelled as everyone boarded this fine looking new toy. With the lines cast off, the yacht beneath their feet, she slowly moved out of the berth and away from the dock. They were underway on this maiden voyage. The children were so excited, boats were honking and blowing their horns, Barbra was grinning from ear-to-ear. Tom stepped into the pilot house, slapping Bob on the shoulder, congratulating him on his newest accomplishment, if a new toy is to be counted as such. After cruising through the bay and passing through the jetties that would lead to the ocean, about 90 minutes since departing the dock, something seemed to go wrong. The new, shining yacht had just entered the ocean when it happened. The massive boat was not steering correctly. First, it was barely noticeable, then the yacht's behavior became more erratic.

Bob screamed over the intercom for a report from the engineer. The controls were not responding; the erratic motion ceased and the boat seemed to be going in a very slow but consistent turn. The engineer came rushing into the pilot house and said, "Sir, we have had a mechanical failure in the rudder control box." Bob screamed, "In plain English, please." The engineer calmly restated, "Sir, the rudders are jammed, we cannot steer."

The man at the helm then yelled, "Sir, we are heading for the rocks at the entrance of the channel."

Bob's wife and children came running into the pilot house yelling, "The boat is breaking, something is wrong, we are going in the wrong direction. Daddy, there are rocks ahead, what is wrong?" Bob, looking like a man with no answers, asked the engineer, "Can't you fix this? All the technology and power of this ship and we are heading toward the rocks."

The engineer, with a somber face, looked Bob straight in the eyes and said, "Sir, it is not the technology or engine power that controls the direction of the ship. It is the rudders. And the rudders are locked in the wrong direction."

Bob sat straight up in his cot in the humble cabin. The old man was asleep on another cot. The fire was still burning, much more dimly than before. Bob wondered, all that I am surrounded with and I have a nightmare about a boat and endangering my family! What is this strangeness - is it guilt or insight - that is the question on my mind?

"Even strength must bow to wisdom sometimes."

— Rick Riordan

8

"YOU ARE WHAT YOU SEEK, THE ANSWER LIES WITHIN"

Bob awoke just as the night was becoming day. Daylight was appearing outside, the sun was not yet up, he guessed it was about an hour from rising. The old man was sitting in front of the fire in his meditation position. Bob removed the covers and then remembered his nightmare. He quietly moved over to the fire and, without saying a word, sat next to the old man in the same position.

Bob thought, how awful to have a nightmare in such a wonderful place. Then he just sat quietly as the sun began to rise. The old man said, *"You are what you seek, the secret lies within."*

Bob said almost whispering, "I understand what you say is true, but I am not sure I am ready or able to find the key to the answers I seek." Before the old man could speak, Bob said, "Sir, I had a dream, sort of a nightmare."

Without moving, the old man just sat there as if he had a hundred years to listen. Bob then relayed the dream, remembering and explaining every detail. After finishing Bob asked, "Is this why I am here, because I have no direction, no rudder? I do not *see* what you *see*, I do not *hear* what you *hear*." He continued, "I do understand the problem, I am grateful and better that I now know what I did not know, I am nonetheless still unable to see the key, the secret."

Nothing more was said. The old man did not move, he did not change his expression or move a muscle.

The old man then put another log on the fire, the flames picked up almost on cue with his starting to talk. "Bob, you are not a rudderless ship, you are simply a man who has lost his way. Hitting the rocks is not your destiny unless you choose that to be your destiny. You speak as if you have no control of the world you live in or choose to live in. You feel you are lost.

As long as you feel lost and act lost then you, my friend, are lost. If you feel you are broken, then you are broken. You do not need a wise old man in the mountains so far from home to tell you all you have, or what you need to do.

"The knowledge, talents and wisdom you seek, the ability to *see* and *hear* what you do not, were gifts given to you at birth by God, accessible to you whenever you choose to use them. Is it not the time for you to learn what you do not know; to know what you have always known? Is it not the time to find that which you seek, to *hear* what you do not *hear*, to *see* what you do not *see*? If not now, when? If not here, where?"

Bob knew but did not know, both at the same time, what the man was saying. He knew there was more to him than he had become, making him feel confident he would find what his friend had found. But was traveling to a mountain truly going to make the difference he had seen in Tom? What miraculous transformation was to happen in his remaining days?

As the sun rose, the rays penetrated the cabin like a firestorm. Everything became so bright. The birds started singing, the breeze started blowing, this was to be a beautiful day.

After the eternal silence, Bob was the first to speak. "Sir, I am ready. What do I need to do to complete my journey that many have tried so hard to help me with?"

The old man said, "There is a wooden flute in a fallen tree trunk high on the mountain. You are to take a sleeping bag and the bag from beside the door with three days of food and water. Follow the trail to the left of the porch where you entered until you reach the tree line. You will then see a number of tree trunks. Take this woodman's carving knife and find the flute, cautiously remove it from the tree trunk and bring it to me. There is a stream close to the clearing, where you can refill your water and refresh yourself. The ancestors of those who live in these mountains say the water from the stream flows from the mountaintop and contains ingredients for mind-clearing and soul-cleansing, so that the mind, heart and soul are open to enlightenment. I will be waiting here until you return. We will then discuss the secret to the wisdom you seek."

"We learn from failure, not from success!"

— Bram Stoker

9

A VISIT TO THE STREAM OF ENLIGHTENMENT

Bob followed the trail as instructed, climbing in elevation. The air was crisp, thin, cold, and the surroundings so beautiful. The peacefulness of the walk cleared his mind and opened his thoughts to all kinds of wonderful things. He was missing his wife and children, wondering if they missed him.

He was not sure how much weight he had lost, but the time of eating healthy and not indulging in unhealthy habits was certainly creating the feeling of a new person. At times, refreshing and positive thoughts would flow into his mind; he was constantly having waves of positive energy and feelings. He felt like he was on the path to find that which he sought, but where, when, how would he know? He wondered aloud if he looked as dramatically different as his friend did on his return.

As all these thoughts were running through his mind, he reached the clearing, just above the tree line. It was exactly as the old man had described.

He laid his sleeping bag and supplies down, as he looked around. He was almost overtaken by the peacefulness of the view, the serene surroundings. If wholesomeness, wisdom, and spirituality were to be visible, this is what it would look like. This is so beautiful; I will just sit here for a while before beginning my search.

It then occurred to him: Where did the old man get a flute? He had seen no so such thing in the meager cabin they were staying in. Was it among the tools in the corner of the cabin? Why would you leave a prized possession like that out here in the weather? He was a wise man and everything he spoke of seemed to be plausible.

After a long meditation on that thought, and letting his mind wander, then taking a long drink of water, Bob proceeded to look in and around the tree trunks. He had no idea what size this flute was. After briefly looking in each of the three tree trunks big enough to hold such a prize, he decided to go one by one.

By dark, he had only dissected one tree trunk and there was no sign of anything but bugs and splintered wood in that tree trunk. He built a small fire with the splintered wood, rolled out his sleeping bag, drank the fresh cool water and ate some of his bread. He was exhausted. He soon fell asleep under the beautiful night.

During the night, he again dreamed of the disabled yacht with his family, broke down, drifting to the rocks, his family panicked, all looking to him. He awoke from the reoccurring nightmare to see the light of day starting to crack above the trees in the east. He thought for a minute, what a strange and terrible dream to have repeatedly in such a place. Is it a mental problem or a piece of the solution to the puzzle? He needed to remember to ask the wise old man his thoughts about such an occurrence in this wonderful place, while in such a great state of mind.

As the sun began to appear above the trees, he was up. He first went to the stream to refill his water and refresh his face with the purest water in all the land. Cold and refreshing, so holistic and therapeutic, it was almost like magic how the water made him feel. He recalled his new mentor's description of the stream and the powers his ancestors believed it held. Then he went back to looking for the elusive prized flute.

By mid-afternoon, he had completed the search of the second tree truck and it too lay in pieces, without finding a flute. He thought, how unlucky for me the flute is hidden in the third and final tree trunk - the last possible place!

He sat eating his bread, studying in detail the shredded wood that lay around him. Could I have missed it and that majestic flute is in pieces around me, or worse, already used for firewood? He slowly began the search of the final tree trunk. Then he paused and sat on the tree trunk, just thinking about the flute. He was clearly missing something here. What was this master of thought and introspection trying to tell or teach him? As he drank his calming water, eating delicious home-baked bread, he decided to go to sleep and start afresh at first light.

He rose again before sunrise, feeling better than he had felt in years, mind refreshed and clear. Making one final trip to the stream of enlightenment, he refilled his canteen and splashed water over his head and face. He was ready for this last and final tree trunk. He would find this flute and bring it back to the cabin and please the master of wisdom.

After again searching carefully and methodically for the third day, he sat disappointed with himself and his search. He thought, my mentor is going to be so disappointed in me. I wonder if I am in the wrong place? After the clarity of the prior day, his mind was suddenly full of self-doubt and questions. Was this a mistake? What am I doing? What happens if I spend all this time and money and nothing changes?

Worst, he again thought, could I have shredded the flute with my carpenter's knife? That is not possible! How could I miss a flute, although the size was not mentioned, no way it could be missed, right? For the first time since being on the mountain with his new and wise mentor, Bob was sad. He missed his family, he was disappointed, and now he knew as the sun began to set, he must trek back down the mountain and tell his mentor he either was in the wrong place or worst yet, he had destroyed the flute.

By the time Bob packed up and made his way back down the trail, it was well past dark as he entered the cabin. The old and wise man, a mentor, yes, but so much more, was sitting in front of the fire, in what appeared to be a similar meditation state as before. By the fire was a pot of something cooking. It smelled great.

As he approached, the mentor slowly turned to look at Bob. Bob immediately said, "I am sorry, sir, but either I was in the wrong place or I destroyed the flute you sent me to look for. I am so sorry for disappointing you, failing at this simple task."

Without showing any emotion of approval or disapproval, he motioned for Bob to sit down; he then dipped a ladle into the pot by the fireplace and gave Bob a bowl of warm stew.

He felt so bad but found he was very hungry since smelling the stew. As he ate, the wise man said, "Bob, first, it is not I who is disappointed, it is you. No person can make another person feel any way at all unless we so choose to let them. What is it that you seek, why are you here?"

Bob started to say something and then just thought long and hard for what seemed like a time without end. The wise old man, his mentor, again showed the patience Bob had come to expect; he showed no emotion and waited.

Bob then said, "I seek the peace and tranquility that I have found in these mountains, the wisdom and confidence you seem to always speak from, the health, knowledge and the ability to see the good in all others and share it with all around me, as my friend Tom did."

The wise and patient old man appeared to be in deep thought as if letting what Bob said soak in like oil into wood. He then asked, "You have no idea why you did not find the flute?" Before Bob could answer he continued, "Bob, the reason you could not find and did not see the flute is you were looking too hard. You could see the forest, not the tree, the flock of birds, not the single most beautiful bird in the flock, the pebbles in the stream, not the gem that lay among them. You have been given all that you need, the secret is within. Inside you is the key to eternal happiness, to success beyond your current vision. You do not *see* or *hear*, simply, what *is*. You have the ability to *see* and *hear* all I have discussed with you. You must look deep inside, clear your mind and your thoughts and be open to the enlightenment that is to be. You are ready."

Bob did not know what he felt, but he was sure he had not found what Tom had found, or the many others who had come here before, looking to find themselves. As the old man returned to his meditation, Bob finished his bowl, picked up his sleeping bag and moved outside into the chilly night. He found a place under the stars to gaze, open his mind, feel what was in his heart and meditate on all he had witnessed, heard and seen since arriving in this beautiful country. He thought and then said to the heavens "Thank you God for what I have, what I have experienced and for bringing me to this place at this time."

As the sun rose on Bob's last day in these mountains, the birds began to sing. He was awake, having never slept, the nightmare replayed in his mind repeatedly, but this last time with a different outcome. He thought, how could I be so blind, how could I not *see* and not *hear* the obvious?

He meditated, savoring on his new found enlightenment, time having no measurement. Then he rose and walked, almost glided, into the cabin, invigorated after his night alone in the forest.

The wise man was sitting much as he had most of this visit and in the same position as when Bob set out to see the unseen. Bob sat beside him. After taking a brief look into Bob's eyes, he said, "So you now *see* and *hear* what is?"

"The mind once enlightened cannot again become dark."

— Thomas Paine

10

WHAT WAS NEVER LOST IS FOUND

Bob said calmly but confidently, "Thank you for all you have shared with me in this time we have spent together, you are the kindest and wisest man I have ever met. I am not sure why I have been so honored and blessed to be in your presence for this phase of my life, but you are and have been a most gracious host, mentor, and friend!" The man did not say anything.

Bob then said, "The reason I did not find the flute is it had yet to be fashioned. I suspect that the piece of wood you directed me to could have been, or would have been, an outstanding flute or violin, even a prized guitar made of the finest wood these Himalayan Mountains have to offer. It might have been destined to be played in the hands of a magical musician, maybe in a world-class orchestra in the future if the person holding the carpenter's knife had the vision and fortitude to create such a masterpiece."

The old man then turned and asked, "Is that all you saw while in the solitude of the night, surrounded by these sacred mountains and the presence of those ancestors that walked this land before you or me?"

Bob continued, "No sir, my nightmare returned as a dream or vision, for I was awake, it was not a nightmare at all." He recounted the dream again, realizing he had now had it many times while on the mountain. He clearly had his wise friend's attention; the man's expression did not change.

Bob told the old man, "As it appeared we were doomed, just as quickly as the panic came, a calm came over me, more precisely to my heart, deep within my soul. "I asked the crew to drop the anchor, the anchor line came taut, the bow turning into the wind, slowly at first, and then we came to a standstill, hundreds of yards from the rocks. The anchor was holding. I asked the engineer if he could repair the gearbox if we could obtain the correct parts. The engineer said he could, so I asked that he radio the boat yard and get the parts sent out to us. We put up a distress flag so other boaters would know we were dead in the water, but not for long! Then I broke out the picnic lunch Barbra had packed.

"With smiles and laughter all around, we had a beautiful day on the water, a wonderful family picnic, enjoying the boating day that was almost a disaster, taking an enjoyable break before restoring our rudder and getting underway."

The wise old man, looking quite pleased, said in his sincerest tone, "I see the student has become the master."

Bob sheepishly said, "I really feel like all of this was so, well, easy. How could I have not seen it before?"

With a smile on his face, the wise old man said, "Bob, we do not know what we do not know until we know, then, my friend, we know forever. The *unseen* becomes the *seen* after we *see*. The *unheard* becomes the *heard* after we *hear*. You see that which you seek is within, or, as a wise old man once said: *You are what you seek, the secret lies within."*

Bob smiled, remembering those very words the day he met the man on the trail into the mountains. Bob started to speak and the man held up a finger to make another point.

"Bob, you and your friend before you, and many of the thousands who have come to these majestic mountains before you came to find that which they sought, only to discover the secret to wisdom, success and eternal happiness were inside of them all the time. Those who do not find what they sought to return to where they came with what they brought, never knowing what was missed. Remember your country's old movie, "The Wizard of Oz?" For Dorothy to find she had the power to return home, she had to make the journey finding out what she did not yet know: There is no place like home, and the power to return home was within her all the time."

Bob now had a single tear of joy, enlightenment, and contentment rolling down his cheek. He did want to go home and share his newfound enlightenment. He wanted to help others as this kind and wise man in the mountains far from home had helped him, as the wise man in the forest had helped Tom. He thought, as he saw the faces of his wife and children in his mind, there *is* no place like home. Peace and tranquility are wherever we make it. In my life, it is at home with my family, having fellowship with my friends and at work with my coworkers, helping them be all they were intended to be. I have traveled thousands of miles to seek a peace, wisdom and insight that I had within all the time. Bob asked the wise old man, his newfound friend, and spiritual mentor, "Can I ask you one more thing before heading home?"

The man, again with a smile, said, "What would that be?"

Bob said, "I wish to do for others what you have done for me, help them *see* the unseen and *hear* the unheard, seeing the world around them with a new perspective, helping people find the wisdom we were born with, the knowledge that lives in our heart and soul as God-given talent."

The old man spoke softly in return, "Bob, as I said, you are now the master. Yes, you will continue to learn and understand more for the rest of your life. However, what you now know, the universal principals of life that you now understand, this new and everlasting enlightenment you have is forever; and it is for sharing with others. It is not and was never intended to be a secret. You will help other people who seek wisdom but do not know where to look. Some you will send here as Tom did you. Others, you will help on your own. I would guess that Tom's friend in the enchanted forest will appear from time to time. Not only will you be able to help others with your newly discovered enlightenment, it is your responsibility to do so. With this knowledge and wisdom comes responsibility.

"You will find with this new you, life at home will go more smoothly, work will have a new light as well. You are destined to prosper. As you now know what you need to succeed is already inside you, you will quickly see only *you* can hold you back. Others will seek your leadership and wisdom; you will help them rise to the occasion, it is what you were intended to do. The enlightened recognize and seek out the enlightened. Those who wish to become more than they have been pursuing the enlightened for guidance and leadership. This makes for success, all those destined to be more than they are, becoming more than they ever dreamed, while taking those who wish to learn and experience with you on the golden path to success and eternity.

"You are the master of your own destiny, becoming the wise old man; it will always be your destiny."

With the conclusion of the conversation and with a smile on both of their faces, the wise old man said, "It is time for you to go home to those you love and miss, and to those who miss and love you. There are lost souls, people waiting to be led to enlightenment and success, awaiting your return."

It was a long walk, Bob did not even notice. He recounted the places he had visited as he walked beside his mentor and friend back down the mountain. Occasionally they would pass someone from the village where Bob had stayed on the first night and he would wave and say his goodbyes, his humble 'thank you' as he passed.

As they approached the huge rock on the trail, there sat the guide in much the same place he had sat before dismissal by the wise old man.

The old man stopped before reaching the guide. He turned to Bob, pulling something out of his robe. "Bob, you have come far; you have been deep inside yourself to *see* what was never seen. As I told you on the mountain, this that you have discovered is and will be yours forever. For you did not find it in these mountains, you brought it with you and then discovered all that you now know here with us. As a token to remember this journey, I give you this stone from high in the mountain, that is much like you were. It is a stone of much beauty, but you cannot see the beauty because of scratches generated by time, dust and dirt that need to be removed. It needs to be polished. Without those acts, sunlight has not been allowed to shine through and expose beautiful rays of light yet to appear. There is little difference between a stone, scratched and dirty, and a priceless gem, for those who have the vision and wisdom to see."

With that, the old man wished Bob great success in his journey. With a smile and a pat on the back, the wise old man, mentor, and friend, turned and disappeared back up the trail.

The guide said to Bob, "You look different my friend, time to go home?" Bob smiled, taking one last look at his surroundings and feeling the joy and enlightenment this experience, these mountains, had brought him.

Without a word, slapping the guide on the back, he started down the trail to his newfound life in a faraway place called home.

Filled with joy, excitement, fresh, pure thoughts and knowledge, he could not wait to see and share them with all those he would come in contact with. It was most hard to believe that all of this was within him all along. Today is the beginning of the rest of this journey we call life.

"There are moments when troubles enter our lives and we can do nothing to avoid them. But they are there for a reason. Only when we have overcome them will we understand why they were there."

— Paulo Coelho

EPILOGUE

Bob made the long flight home, to the waiting open arms of his wife Barbra and three children. He had lost weight and had an aura about him. Tom stopped over, gave him a big hug and said, "We will talk soon." Yet nothing else really needed to be said between them.

Bob returned to work the following Monday, instantly scheduling the next family fun day for the employees. At his next staff meeting, with his managers and other executives in attendance, he listened to everyone, gave a few pointed suggestions, and asked to meet with everyone individually in the coming weeks. When asked about stagnate sales, slumping morale and dipping productivity, Bob simply stated, "I have a vision for what needs to be done. I will be sharing it with you and all the company associates during regular meetings, as well as ongoing one-on-one meetings. We are all on the road to the success this company is destined for."

After the completion of the meeting, many in attendance thanked him for commencing the employee family day in the coming month. Everyone congratulated him on how great he looked and what extraordinary input he had provided. It was clear to all who attended, they were on a new path, that all waited with anticipation the details of his vision for restoring the company to greatness. As Bob was walking out of the conference room, the CEO, who had not attended the meeting, stuck his head around the corner and asked if he could have a word.

The CEO told him in a very somber voice, "Bob, I wanted to tell you something, I had every intention of releasing you from your duties on your return. I received a phone call from a friend who owns a business downtown, he told me of an incident you were involved in, it could have gone several ways. However, it appears that the incident in question seems to have put you on a different path. The feedback I am hearing from managers and employees in the short time since you returned, the buzz, almost excitement, all about some miraculous transformation, I had to see this for myself. What is your secret, you look great, are you going to share it?"

Without a second to think, Bob simply said, "It is my destiny to share what I have learned.

As they say, before every airplane takes off, "When the oxygen masks drop, put your mask on first, then assist those around you."

He continued, "I learned that finding one's self takes looking inside one's self. If you clear your mind, distrust or ignore unhealthy thoughts and search your soul, it is amazing what you might discover. In other words, 'You are what you seek, the secret lies within.'"

With that, the CEO asked Bob if he and Barbra could join him and his wife for dinner at the club this coming weekend. Bob walked out of the office door saying, "We would be honored, just name the time." The CEO smiled big and said, "Bob, we have much to talk about. I want to hear all about this newfound vision you have for *our* company."

The End

AUTHOR'S NOTE

While this is a fable, it is based on life experiences of friends, mentors and myself. Some were personally experienced; some learned from others. The intent of this fable is to illustrate that through tragedy or self-induced problems comes self-development, enlightenment, and happiness if a person desires change and is open to all that can be.

Personal tragedy, bad judgment, and mistakes do not define us; they are the stepping stones in life's journey that lead us to an understanding of principles that are larger than ourselves. God has gifted each of us with talents; it is up to us to develop the wisdom and humility to act on the intention of these talents. Can you answer "yes" to the questions: Are you who you were destined to be? Are you happy and fulfilled in all you have become?

This book highlights when we slow down and clear our mind, we will discover our inner wisdom. There is no connection between inner wisdom and IQ or education, it is inside our hearts and minds since birth. Alcohol, drugs, and personal tragedy can dull inner wisdom, learning from and moving past these crises define who we are.

It is my goal to help others uncover the reality that we are who we are, we act the way we act because of our thoughts and ourselves. To say someone caused us to act in a way contrary to our inner wisdom is to give them power over us.

You and you alone, can optimize the influence of your state of mind and reflect on your intended destiny. You and you alone, are responsible for your actions. Actions are based on thoughts, habits, and judgments. You have the ability to discover your inner wisdom and thus be the person you were created to be.

It is my hope and desire that Bob's journey confirms the power of reflection, along with questioning of thoughts and assumptions as worthy tools to help you realize and exercise your wisdom. It is through inner wisdom that you will perform the intentions of your talents, find happiness in all that you do, and help others along the way.

ACKNOWLEDGEMENTS

I would like to give thanks to all who contributed to my vision and knowledge that became the makings of this book. Thank you, God, for the insight, blessings and thousands of guardian angels provided my entire life, and for the intuition to write this book.

Thank you to the editor, Cheryl Schmidt, a great friend, superior editor and the godmother to my son, Christopher. Thank you, cover designer, Laura Cooper, who painted the cover after not finding a picture that could give justice to the landscapes described in this book. From your heart to this cover, thank you.

To my wife, Hope, an inspiration to me and to all those she touches and contributes to.

To my longtime pastor, friend, spiritual coach, and confidant, the late Monsignor John P. Caulfield, may you rest in peace, thank you for always being there. "Jesus, I trust in you."

Thank you, Gina Woolf, who entered my life at a most precarious time, teaching the

Second Chance class I attended while in work-release. She keeps me focused on the enlightenment, wisdom, three principles of life, and using them to help others.

SPECIAL ACKNOWLEDGEMENT

To my parents, Randy and Joyce: My father, may he rest in peace, was always a steady hand of encouragement and understanding. My mom, with her strength and a giving heart, has always been there. I love you both. Thank you for the freedoms to succeed and fail all at the same time. It made me stronger and wiser.

.

ABOUT THE AUTHOR

Michael R Holley Born in Panama City Florida on December 26, 1960, Michael started from solid but humble beginnings. The son, grandson, nephew, and cousin of boat captains. Working his way from deckhand to captain, at the young age of nineteen. That was not to be his destiny. By chance, an advertisement for a car salesman at the age of twenty-one was about to change his life forever.

From showroom floor to owning his own businesses, accumulating three franchise automotive dealerships in central Florida, only to have it all crumble in the financial crisis of 2008 losing all worldly positions and ultimately his freedom. Instead of allowing this to define his life, he thanks God for the lessons he has learned and the guardian angels that brought him through this journey. Michael's life now has a whole new meaning. Helping others and sharing knowledge, wisdom and insight. Currently consulting with business owners, helping them and their managers and successors see life and business with a new perspective. Mentoring family and non-family managers/successors. Analyzing current business operations, profitability, and coaching on how to expand retail, business to business and commercial sales. Teaching business owners, franchise auto dealers and managers how to recruit, hire, train and retain Gen Y/Millennial while building a culture to retain more employees.

Giving public and private speeches to churches, civic organizations, trade associations and conventions. Entertaining business groups while helping them see business and life through a new perspective. Michael is currently working on a number of upcoming publishing projects. In this journey, we call life he is very proud to now be referred to as an author, speaker, business consultant and mentor, here to help others see the path to enlightenment, happiness and success.

Please see Michael's LinkedIn profile for speaking and consulting. Follow him at www.michaelholley.com, Facebook, LinkedIn, and Twitter.

To contact Michael R. Holley: Michael@ michaelholley.com

To book speaking engagements, business consulting, business/life coaching, private book signings, speak at your corporate meeting/convention, private events; Call Hopeful Publishing at (863) 559-4049, send an inquiry using the web form at www. michaelholley.com/book-michael, or email bookmichael@michaelholley.com.

Michael's blog at www.michaelholley.com/blog
Friend him on Facebook, LinkedIn, Twitter, and Goodreads

Michael R. Holley
Business Consultant, Speaker, Author,
Recruiting/Hiring Guru
email:Michael@michaelholley.com

Pricing for Speaking, Consulting and Business/Life Coaching on request.

Books from Hopeful Publishing Company, Inc.
P.O. Box 7517
Lakeland, FL 33807
By Michael R. Holley

MICHAEL R HOLLEY

http://www.amazon.com/Michael-R-Holley/e/
B00R0GD0KO

"Pinstripe Suits to Prison Blues" In Print,
Kindle, Audio at Amazon.com
"Finding the Wisdom You Seek" In Print and
Kindle at Amazon.com
"Using the Wisdom You Found" Fall 2016
"Life after the Loss; The Rest of the Story"
2017
There is a book inside of you, write it!

Speaking to and inspiring those desiring to
be all they were destined to be!

Hopeful Publishing Company, Inc.